for Ryan and Kevin

Requests for permission to make copies of any part of the work should be submitted online at info@mascotbooks.com or mailed to Mascot Books, 560 Herndon Parkway #120, Herndon, VA 20170

PRT1113A

Printed in the United States.

Library of Congress Control Number: 2013950822

ISBN-13: 9781620864593
ISBN-10: 1620864592

www.mascotbooks.com

Oops Paint

Kathryn Horn Coneway

One day I decided to make a painting. My mom put out my colors - red, blue, and yellow - on a paper plate on the table.

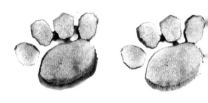

I went to get my smock. While I was gone, someone curious jumped up on the table.

Oops! When I came back I found this painting made by my...

Cat.

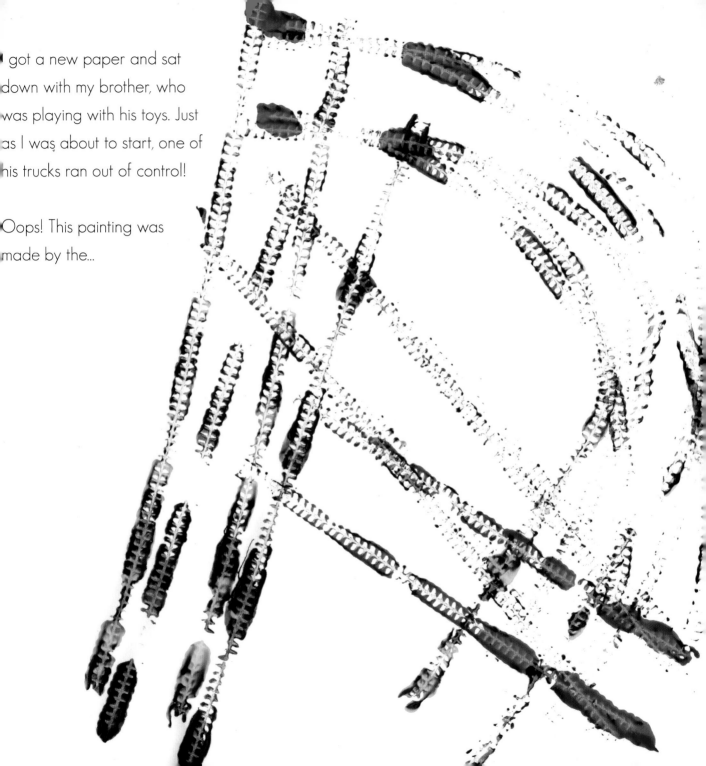

I got a new paper and sat down with my brother, who was playing with his toys. Just as I was about to start, one of his trucks ran out of control!

Oops! This painting was made by the...

Truck's Tires.

I decided to try working
on the floor where no one
would bother me. My sister
came running in and didn't
see what I was doing.

Oops! This painting was
made by her...

Shoes.

I moved to the porch to join my grandmother, who was sewing. Just as I was about to start again, she sneezed and dropped her work.

Oops! This painting was made by her...

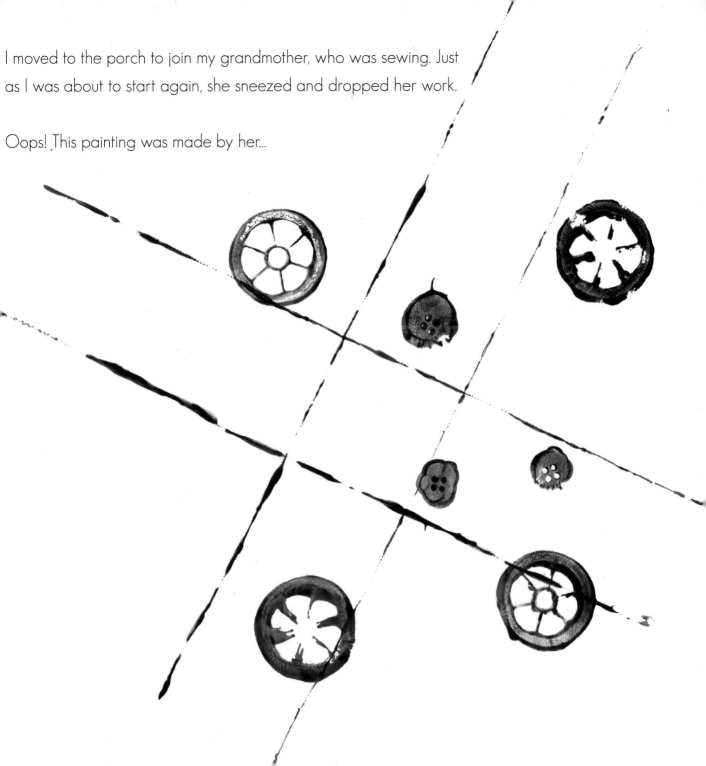

Buttons and Thread.

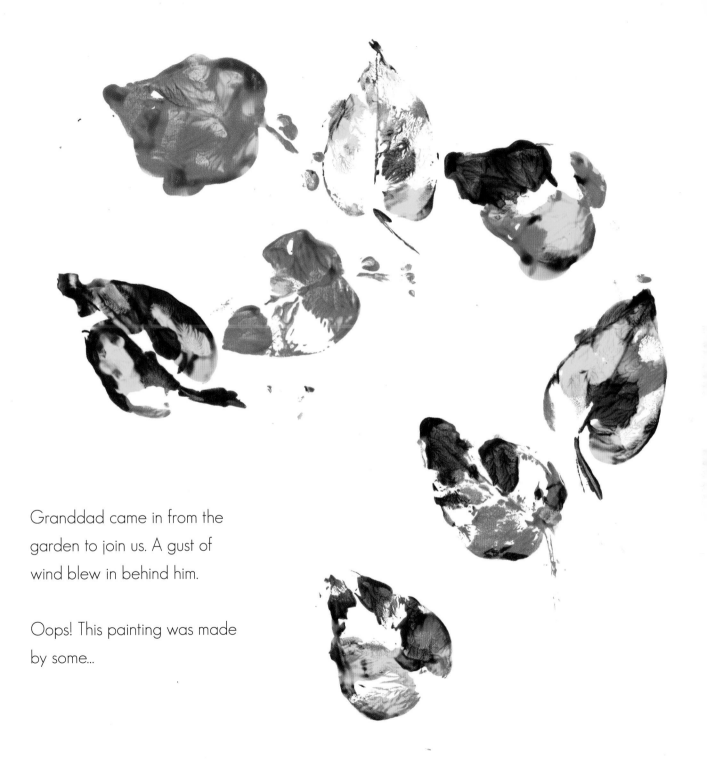

Granddad came in from the garden to join us. A gust of wind blew in behind him.

Oops! This painting was made by some...

Leaves.

Dad brought me a snack, but I dropped a piece right in the paint.

Oops! This painting was made by my...

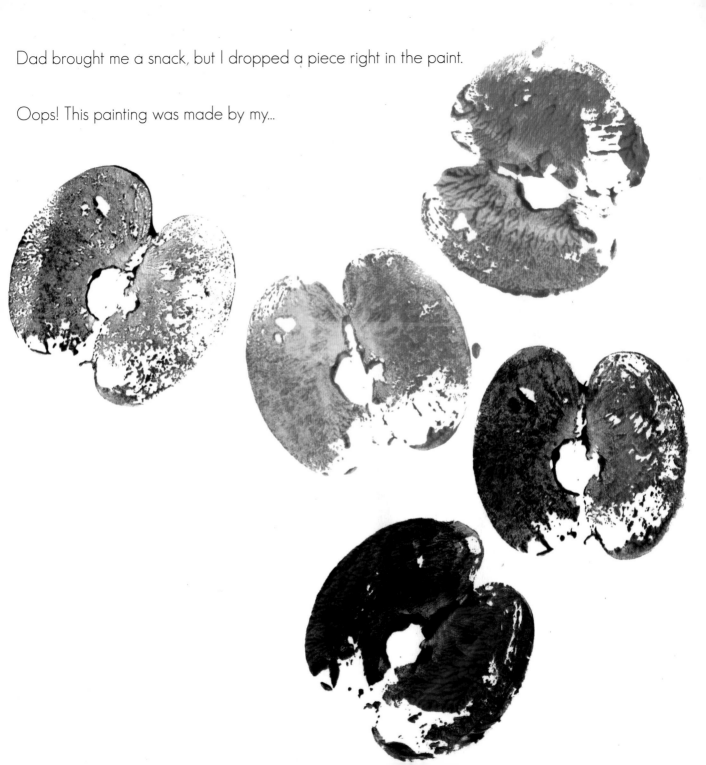

Apple.

Mom reached in to help, but
her bracelet slipped off and
fell in the paint.

Oops! This painting was
made by her...

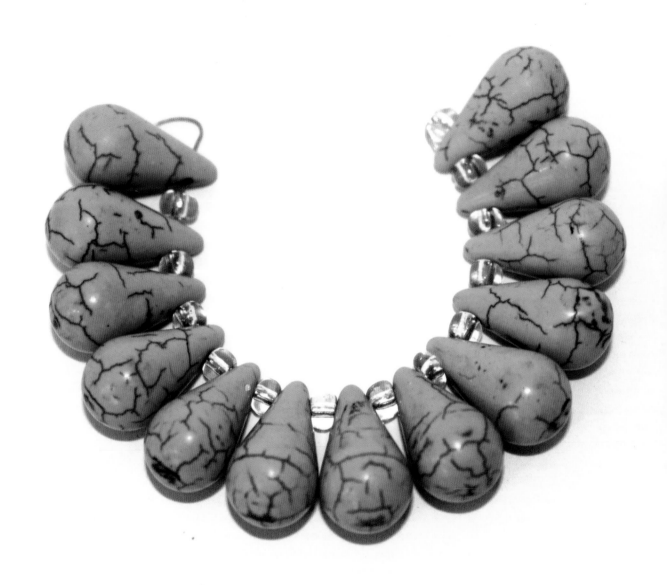

Beads.

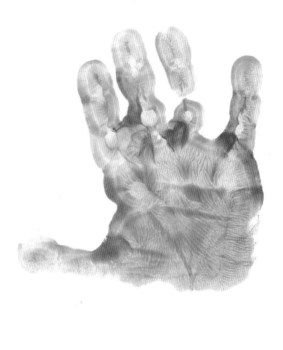

Finally, it was my turn. I made this painting with my...

Hands.

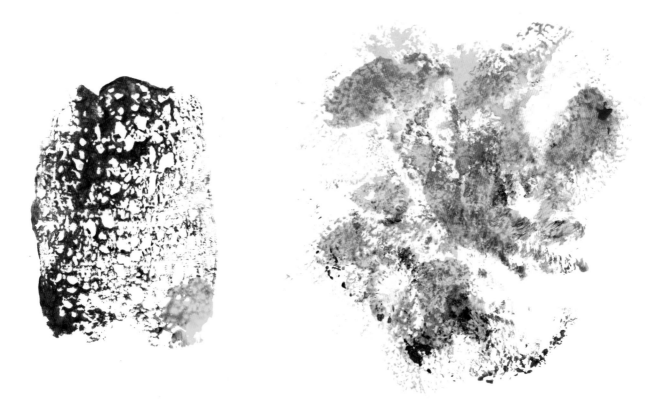

Mom helped me clean up my hands with a towel and Dad wiped the table clean with a sponge. When they set them down they made two final paintings. Can you tell which is which?

Then, my whole family came to admire our
beautiful paintings.

Which one is your favorite?

What else could we drop in the paint?

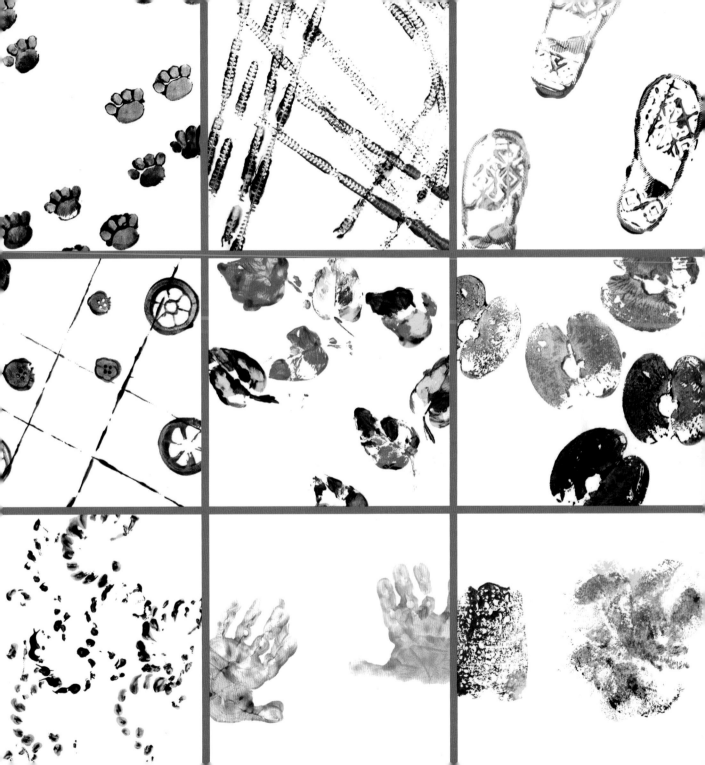

Can you match these household objects to the prints they made?

Can you match these toys to the
prints they made?

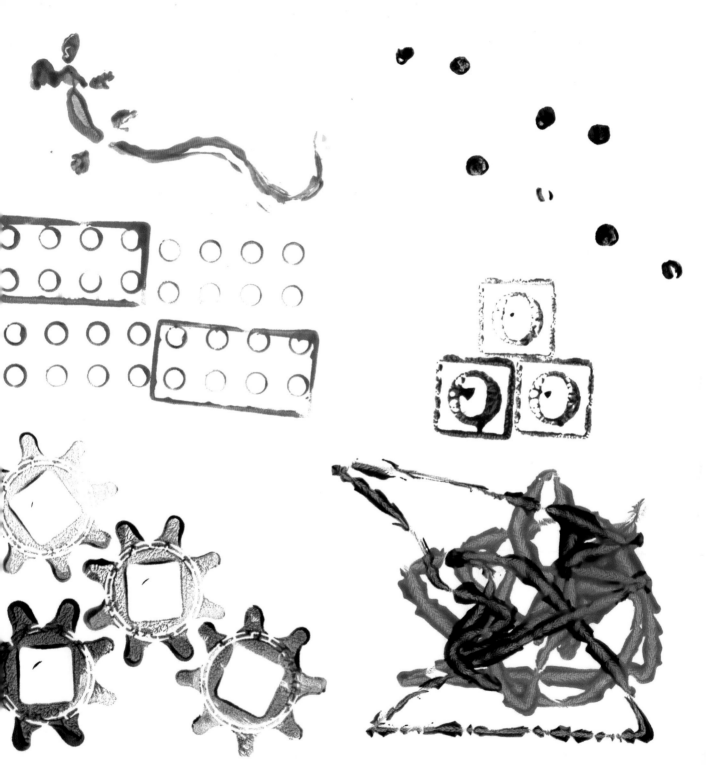

Can you match these recycled objects to the prints they made?

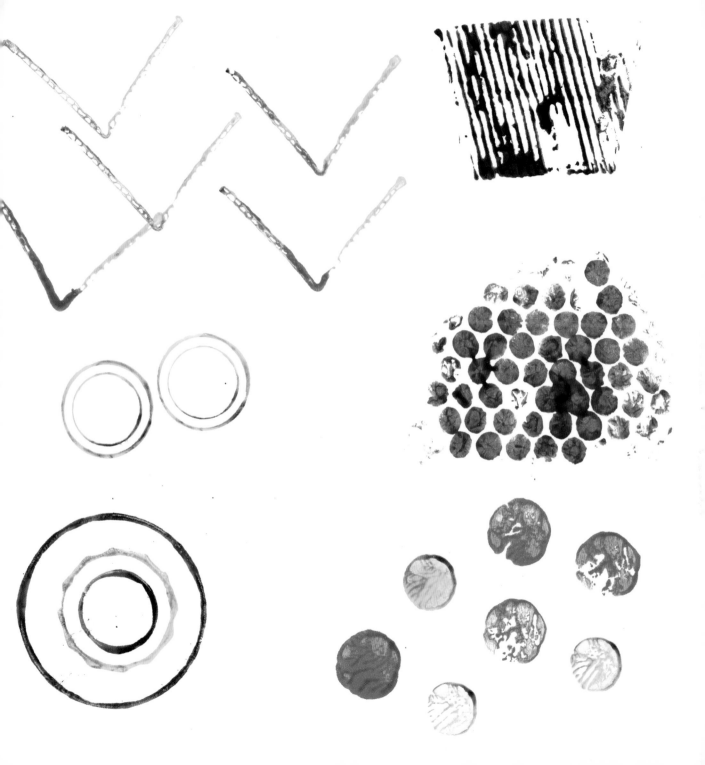

A collection of objects stamped
together can make a picture.

Look for prints you recognize from objects on earlier pages.

A note for parents, teachers, and other creative companions...

This book was inspired by many experiences teaching art workshops to parents and toddlers. Stamping with everyday objects is always a favorite activity and a great way to explore shape, texture, and color with young children.

When working in the home studio, a paper plate with puddles of paint works well and can allow children to mix colors as they stamp. Placing your paper on a pad of newspapers will offer a cushion and greater definition in your stamped marks.

I like to begin with just a few simple objects and add new things as we go. Trucks and toy animals create great tracks. Objects like spools and blocks offer the ability to print from different sides. Once you start printing, you will find yourself looking at objects and textures in entirely new ways. Children may also enjoy drawing on and around their prints once they dry.

Let your child guide you as you explore together. You may be surprised by the ideas they come up with. Also, let your child participate in set-up and clean-up; experiencing every step of the process is important in their development as artists.

Thank you for letting me share this story with you. Please share your own printing and stamping ideas at oopspaint@artatthecenter.org.

Thanks, Kathryn

About the Author

Kathryn Horn Coneway is the director of Art at the Center, a studio lab for children and families in Alexandria, Virginia. She originally wrote *Oops Paint* when she was unable to find a book about printing that was simple enough for toddlers to understand. The first draft of the book lived in the studio for a couple of years, where Kathryn enjoyed watching families read it together and find inspiration in its pages. She hopes *Oops Paint* will spark ideas for printing and stamping, and encourage relationship building through art making and storytelling.

Kathryn lives in Alexandria, Virginia with her husband, Chad, and two sons, Ryan and Kevin. She has a dog named Kona and good memories of her cat, Bagel.

Did your cat really help make the book?

Yes and No

YES, the idea of a cat walking through paint was inspired by my real cat, Bagel. When he was a kitten he was very shy. One morning I woke up to find little cherry juice paw prints all around my paper on the drawing table. It was fun to know that while he kept his distance during the day, he was at least a bit curious about me and what I was doing.

NO, I did not use Bagel's feet to make the images in the book. They were made from a simple stamp created with pieces of foam rubber stuck to a block of wood. I made the stamp when I was a child and wanted to be able to sign letters as if they were from a cat.

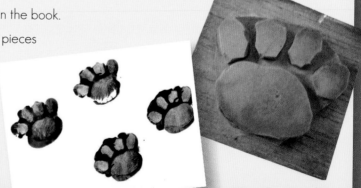